Tiny Tig

AT HOME IN THE JU

ILLUSTRATED BY KRISTA BRAUCKMANN-TOWNS
WRITTEN BY JENNIFER BOUDART

Copyright © 1995 Publications International, Ltd.
ISBN 0-7853-1216-1
Leap Frog is a trademark of Publications International, Ltd.

It is morning in the jungle. Steam rises up from the ground. Jungle plants sparkle with dew. Monkeys and birds chatter in the treetops. It's a morning just like any other morning. Or is it?

Look! Three tiger cubs come tumbling out of their dark cave. Today is their first day outdoors. They are eight weeks old and ready to explore.

The bright sun makes the young cubs blink. Their eyes are used to the darkness of their cave home. A monkey screams, and two cubs scramble for cover.

The third cub is smaller, but much braver, than her brothers. She looks for the monkey.

Her name is Tiny Tiger, and one day she will grow up to be a beautiful tigress. 🐾🐾

A low grunting sound brings all three cubs running. They know the sound of their mother's voice.

Tiny Tiger and her brothers follow Mother Tiger through the tall jungle grass. Their stripes hide them very well. To other animals, they look like swaying grasses filled with shadows and sunlight. 🐾🐾

The family comes up to a small lake. It is quiet, cool, and shady—perfect for the hot tigers. First, Mother Tiger checks the area for danger. No jackals or jaguars. Just a few harmless little birds.

The three young tigers have never been swimming. Like all tigers, the three cubs love water. They march right in! 🐾🐾

The little cubs wrestle and tumble by the cool jungle lake. Tiny Tiger sees a peacock.

She takes a few steps toward the beautiful bird. It flies away! Tiny Tiger thinks the peacock is afraid of her. She is wrong.

The bird has seen something large in the grass. Suddenly, a loud roar freezes Tiny Tiger in her tracks! 🐾🐾

Another tiger is here! The cubs run and hide behind their mother. Mother Tiger is not scared because she knows this visitor. He is Father Tiger. They rub necks to say hello.

Tiny Tiger bravely jumps from behind her mother. She growls a baby growl. Her father gently rubs her with his big paw before going on his way. 🐾🐾

The family returns home for a nap. The cubs cuddle up together in front of their cave. Mother Tiger washes each of the three cubs with her rough tongue. Then she lies down with them to rest.

After her nap, Mother Tiger hunts for food for her little cubs. She leaves them safely napping near the cave. 🐾🐾

Tiny Tiger's legs kick as she sleeps. She flicks her tail and growls softly. She happily dreams about the day when she will grow up to roam the jungle as a mighty tigress. 🐾🐾